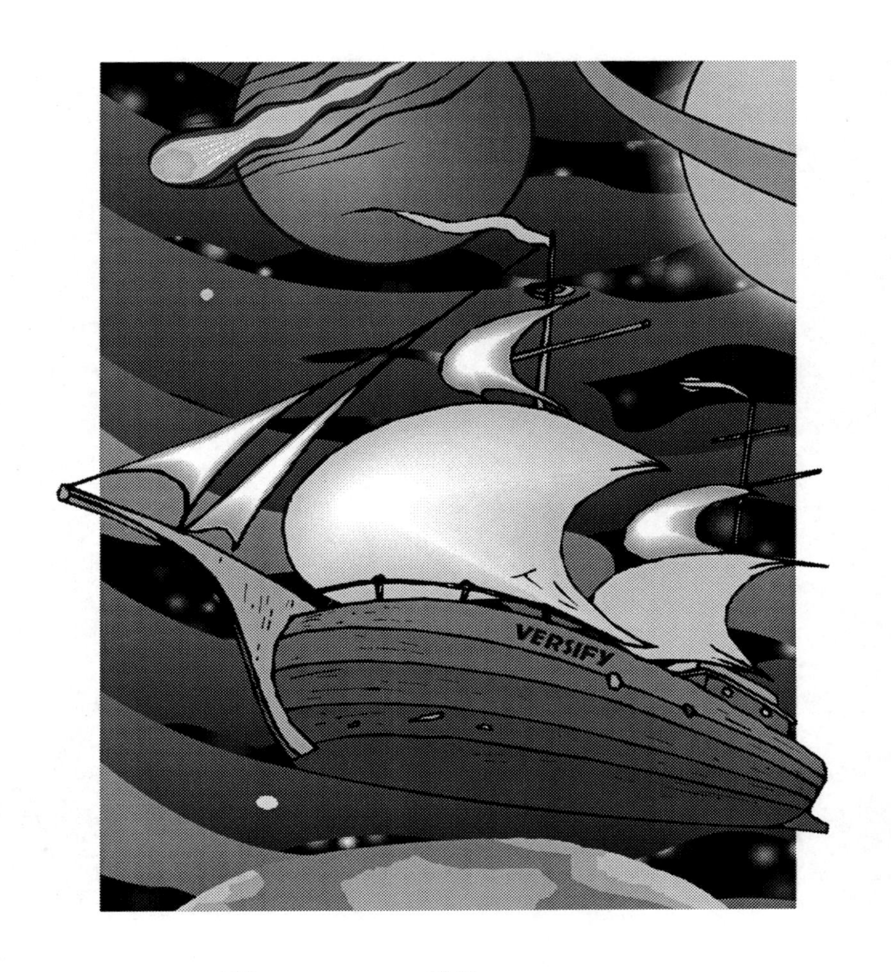

POETIC VOYAGES BALLYMENA

Edited by Lucy Jeacock

First published in Great Britain in 2001 by
YOUNG WRITERS
Remus House,
Coltsfoot Drive,
Peterborough, PE2 9JX
Telephone (01733) 890066

All Rights Reserved

Copyright Contributors 2001

HB ISBN 0 75433 098 2
SB ISBN 0 75433 099 0

FOREWORD

Young Writers was established in 1991 with the aim to promote creative writing in children, to make reading and writing poetry fun.

This year once again, proved to be a tremendous success with over 88,000 entries received nationwide.

The Poetic Voyages competition has shown us the high standard of work and effort that children are capable of today. It is a reflection of the teaching skills in schools, the enthusiasm and creativity they have injected into their pupils shines clearly within this anthology.

The task of selecting poems was therefore a difficult one but nevertheless, an enjoyable experience. We hope you are as pleased with the final selection in *Poetic Voyages Ballymena* as we are.

Contents

Ballykeel Primary School

Ryan McKendry	1
Dean Boyd	2
Jade Wylie	3
Julie Carleton	4
Adam Jewsbury	5
Joshua Kenny	6
Natasha Crozier	7
Marc Mitchell	8
Madison Graham	9
Elizabeth Brown	10
Colin Halliday	11
Isuara Soleiro	12
Lisa Heaney	13
Krissy McAllister	14
Beverley Millar	15
Noeleen Sloan	16
Stuart Brown	17
Michael Arbuthnot	18
Kim Surgenor	19
Ross Adams	20
Elizabeth Balmer	21
Christopher Shaw	22

Braidside IPS School

Kelly-Ann McAuley	23
Nikki Carlisle	24
Catherine Foley	25
Hannah Harman Ingleton	26
Yong Ki Choi	27
Karas Quinn	28
Michael Byrne	29
Lewis Edwards	30
Richard Tuff	31

Broughshane Primary School

Trevor Weir	32
Charlene Galloway	33
Rachel Duffy	34
Emma Bradley	35
Ian Mark	36
Steven McGall	37
Darren McAlonan	38
Timothy Patton	39
Laura Currie	40
Dean Adams	41
Jessica Boal	42
Jenna Galbraith	43
Philip McBurney	44
Hannah Gibson	45
Josh Boal	46
Patricia Boyd	47
James Martin	48
Katie Wray	49
Howard Jamieson	50
Jane Burgess	51
Lisa-Jane Millar	52
Mark Foster	53
Nigel Elliott	54
Christina Magee	55
Gareth McCullough	56
Keri Smyth	57
Iain Loughridge	58
Cherith O'Hara	59
Peter Thompson	60
Jenny McCandless	61
Ciara Topping	62
David Murray	63
Christopher Smyth	64
Nicole Connor	65
Chloe Kennedy	66
David Nelson	67
Gemma Lindsay	68

Julie-Anne Cairns 69
Mark McNeill 70
Kathryn Thompson 71
Peter Gilmore 72
Cathryn Maybin 73
Cara Faith 74
Katrina Douglas 75
Ashley McCandless 76
Christopher McClean 77
Emma Graham 78
Philip Smyth 79
Grant Campbell 80
Tanya Wilson 81
David Evans 82
Steven Mairs 83
Nicole Bradley 84
Michelle Finlay 85
Christine Maybin 86
Kathryn O'Hara 87
Evie Carrington 88
Andrew Duffy 89
Jason Paul 90
Jill Robinson 91
Rachel Harkness 92
Jack Burgess 93
Amy Coleman 94
Jodie Calderwood 95
Rachel Mairs 96
Kathryn Hamilton 97
Laura Finlay 98
Catherine Chambers 99
Janine Mark 100
Kathryn Gilmore 101
Hannah McCooke 102

Moorfields Primary School
Joanne Fleck 103
Brian McCartney 104

Richard Campbell 105
Philip Houston 106
Emma Ayre 107
Zoë Moore 108
Hayley McKeown 109
Aaron McAuley 110
Louise Cooper 111
Andrew Munce 112
Craig McCullough 113
Steven McCammond 114
Ruth Barr 115
Deborah Fleck 116
Philip Moffett 117
Ryan Kerr 118
David Fleck 119
David Campbell 120
Emma Cameron 121
Anna Caldwell 122

St Mary's Primary School

Lucy McLaughlin 123
Johnnie McKillop 124
Carmel McCambridge 125
Patrick McLaughlin 126
Ann Burke 127
Niamh Horscroft 128
Jordan Delaney 129
Paul Smart 130
Matthew Bowen 131
Rita O'Neill 132
Eamon O'Neill 133
Mark Donaghy 134
Stephen Donaghy 135
Maria AcAllister 136
Seamus McNaughton 137
Alison McKeggan 138
Ciara Frances McAllister 139
Aidan McNaughton 140

Patricia J McNaughton 141
Joanne Stewart 142
Ciara-Helen McAllister 143
Mary McAteer 144
Aoife Quinn 145
Jessica Gillan 146
Fiona McAlister 147
Emma Duignan 148
Ciara Campbell 149
Michael Kane 150
Kathryn McAlister 151
Jane Molloy 152
Anne-Marie Fleet 153
Caolan Carson 154
Alexandra McLaughlin 155
Tessa McDonnell 156
Bronagh Heggarty 157

St Patrick's Primary School
Brian McMullan 158
Catriona McLean 159
Emma McKean 160
Francis O'Neill 161
Connor McGilligan 162
Celine O'Kane 163
Jezamine Pressly 164
Rosemarie McKeown 165
Conor McMullan 166
Bridget McGinty 167
Catherine McGarry 168
Thérèse Tunney 169
Pam-Eileen McLean 170
Eimeár McCoy 171
Bronagh Kelly 172
Leona McAllister 173
Donna Robinson 174
Kevin Agnew 175
Maura O'Mullan 176

Laura Glendinning 177
James O'Kane 178
Leanne Dickson 179
Helen Doherty 180
Mark McGuiggan 181
Patrick Tunney 182
Claire McMullan 183
Donagh McAllister 184
Laura O'Kane 185
Sharon Kelly 186
Caitriona Hasson 187
Reece McLaughlin 188
Catherine O'Kane 189
Enda Drain 190
Ryan Doherty 191
Clare Kelly 192
Meghan Rafferty 193
Terry O'Boyle 194
Eugene McTaggart 195

The Diamond Primary School
Emma McKay 196
Jason Harkness 197
Andrew Byers 198
Stuart Thompson 199
Amy Greer 200
Beverley Kerr 201
Zoey Peacock 202
Hollie Thompson 203

The Poems

HELP

P ick a poem - hard to choose
O h, which one should I use?
E verybody has one to choose
M e, the silly one sitting here
S omeone help me, it's hard to choose
Please help me or I will lose.

Ryan McKendry (10)
Ballykeel Primary School

BROTHER'S OUT!

He's the best
Says my uncles
He's great!
I wish he'd disappear
I'd love to sell him
He's a waste of space
Take him away
Please
Take him away.

Dean Boyd (10)
Ballykeel Primary School

BROTHER LOVE

I love my brother when he is good
I hate him when he is bad
I wish someone would come and take him away please,
Please, please
I don't want to be left here with him
I just don't like him because he hits me
I just want rid of him.

Jade Wylie (10)
Ballykeel Primary School

WINTER

Christmas Eve morning
I watched the snow go down as
The mist blew around.

Julie Carleton (10)
Ballykeel Primary School

WAITING FOR SANTA

Walking through the fog
On a lonely winter night
Waiting for Santa.

Adam Jewsbury (9)
Ballykeel Primary School

Winter

Sledging in the snow
Kissing under mistletoe
Happy Christmas.

Joshua Kenny (9)
Ballykeel Primary School

WINTER

It is Christmas time
The robins sing in the trees
Santa leaves some toys.

Natasha Crozier (9)
Ballykeel Primary School

WINTER NIGHT

Looking at the stars
on an icy winter night
and rain falling down.

Marc Mitchell (9)
Ballykeel Primary School

My Mad Family

Mummies always want you to look nice and clean,
Uncles just embarrass you,
Brothers are always mean.

Sisters always steal your things and hide them in their room,
Aunties always kiss you in the living room,
Cousins always come and try to steal your toys,
This is my mad family, girls and boys.

Madison Graham (9)
Ballykeel Primary School

Winter Time

Snow falls through the night
I like playing in the snow
Having snowball fights.

Elizabeth Brown (9)
Ballykeel Primary School

RECIPE FOR WINTER

Take 2 platefuls of Christmas dinner
and add 1 cupful of home-made soup,

Add memories of Christmas Day
and pike fishing,

Mix 1 bowl full of icicles with 500ml of slush
and 6 tablespoons of holly and sprinkle a pinch
of snowflakes and 18 inches of snow,

Bake in the hailstones for 11 hours
and serve.

Serves approximately 6-7 people
and you have made Winter.

Colin Halliday (10)
Ballykeel Primary School

SIMON

Take my brother
Please
He's driving me insane
Take him away quick before
I do something I'll regret
I've had it up to my ears
But today he was very kind
I won't sell him for a penny
But get him away
For 50p.

Isaura Soleiro (9)
Ballykeel Primary School

Summer

Lovely sunny days
The sun is shining brightly
Children on the beach.

Lisa Heaney (9)
Ballykeel Primary School

CAPTURE!

I want to capture the sound of Britney Spears.
I want to capture the feel of my auntie's spiky hair.
I want to capture the smell of my baby cousin's clean head.
I want to capture the sight of my special book.
I want to capture the taste of pepperoni pizza.
I want to capture the moment when my little brother
called me sissy.
I want to capture the memory of my first day when
I was over in England.
I want to capture the silence of everyone asleep in
bed at home.
I want to capture the feeling of happiness and excitement
when it is my birthday.

Krissy McAllister (9)
Ballykeel Primary School

SISTERS

I hate my sister
She's driving me mad
Last night when I went to bed to sleep
She came into my room
And beat me up.

But then again I love her
When she gets me a drink
And says I love you
Thanks, I say
And give her a hug.

Beverley Millar (10)
Ballykeel Primary School

Recipe For Winter

Take 29 kilograms of snow
and 2 months of winter holidays,

Add 2 days of mist
and fog,

Mix hailstones
and rain,

And stir for 5 mins,

Bake for 2 hours and
then have *fun!*

You have made Winter.

Noeleen Sloan (10)
Ballykeel Primary School

SISTERS

I'll tell you about my sister
She drives me up the wall!
She won't even play ball with me
I wish she'd disappear.

Though today she was really sweet,
But only because she wanted a sweet.
But after I gave her what she wanted,
She treated me like a pig!

I hate my sister lots and lots
She's really nasty,
I need someone to take her away,
. . . I've got money.

Stuart Brown (10)
Ballykeel Primary School

He's So Perfect

My big brother annoys me all day
He shouts and yaps and takes my things
My mum always says he's the perfect boy
But I think she is talking a lot of rubbish

The only thing I like about my brother
Is when he gives me sweets and money
But when he is fast asleep I wish I could
Hit him with a jar of out-of-date honey.

Michael Arbuthnot (9)
Ballykeel Primary School

WINTER

Playing in the snow
Putting up the Christmas tree
Cold frosty mornings.

Kim Surgenor (9)
Ballykeel Primary School

My Important Little Sister

People say she's good
but I think she's bad,

she throws my money
down the toilet,
and people say she's so pretty,
but they say to me
why can't you be as good as your sister.

She is alright sometimes
and that is at night-time.

Ross Adams (10)
Ballykeel Primary School

SUMMER

S un is shining in the warm sky
U mbrellas are in the bin
M aking burgers on the barbecue
M aking ice creams for the children
E xciting things to do
R elaxing on the beach.

Elizabeth Balmer (9)
Ballykeel Primary School

LUNCH

L ollipops in your lunch
U mbrellas are nice
N ice friends being kind
C ats wanting cat food
H ome, home, nice to be home.

Christopher Shaw (10)
Ballykeel Primary School

My Cousin T

My cousin is very funny
She really likes sweet bee honey
She is really kind
She really has a good mind
Her hair is brown
Her eyes are blue
She would like to play with you.

Kelly-Ann McAuley (8)
Braidside IPS School

My Daddy

My daddy is funny, silly and kind
Always on time, when he's needed
I'm like a volcano when he comes in
He's almost bald
That's my dad, yes it is!
He's the best, and he's fun to play with.

Nikki Carlisle (8)
Braidside IPS School

The Sunny Day

It was Sunday
and it was sunny
no clouds in the sky at all.

It was Sunday
and the day was as
bright as ever.

It was Sunday
and the day was so, so hot
the sea was hot too.

It was Sunday
it was hot, so I went to bed
in the afternoon instead.

Catherine Foley (8)
Braidside IPS School

My Granny

My granny is tall, thin and very funny,
She can do the dishes and also be funny,
She is very old-fashioned and not very strict.

My granny has blue eyes and pretty hair,
She always has sweets lurking somewhere,
I think I know where they are, in a cupboard tall and far.

My granny can make Granny Soup, I don't like it but they do,
She makes tomato soup just as well as making Granny Soup.

I love my granny.

Hannah Harman Ingleton (8)
Braidside IPS School

ALONE

My mum's as sweet as an orange,
She's the only thing I need,
She's always tired.

She is the fire in my chimney,
She's the ash from my coal,
She just loves grey.

She likes talking to me,
If there's no mum like this, I think I'll cry,
I really love her.

She loves doing art with me,
I don't know what I could do without her,
She just loves to hear my voice.

Yong Ki Choi (9)
Braidside IPS School

My Daddy

My daddy is nice to me and funny as well,
he has blond hair.

My dad lets me get away with things,
his eyes are bright green.

He is nice to everyone he knows now,
he is the king of the house.

I love my daddy.

Karas Quinn (8)
Braidside IPS School

SUN

When the sun comes up
it's a great sight.
But I don't get to see it so
therefore I sleep on.

When I get up, Dad turns
on my bedroom light.
But do I mind, no,
it's just like the sun.

Michael Byrne (8)
Braidside IPS School

FOG

The fog is not white,
It is just a haze
Of water in a cloud,
Which hangs around for days.

The fog is low,
A friend of rain,
But to an adult car
It is a pain.

The fog is grey,
A low dry cloud,
But if you ask me
It must be very proud.

Well at long last
The fog is gone,
But you can still hear
Its calming song.

Lewis Edwards (9)
Braidside IPS School

WEATHER

It is raining hard
And flooding high
And we are stuck inside
All the time

It is sunny now
And we can go
Outside all the
Time

It is snowing deep
And we're having
Fun all the time

It is icy and slippy
And fun all the
Time.

Richard Tuff (9)
Braidside IPS School

WINTER/SUMMER

Winter
It is winter in Broughshane
it is very cold
it is very snowy
it is very icy.

Summer
Summer is nice and hot
We play in our paddling pool
And we go on our holidays.

Trevor Weir (8)
Broughshane Primary School

SCHOOL

I'm in primary seven
And I think it's the best
We play and we work
But I don't like doing tests.

I did my transfer test in November
And I thought it was hard
But then I realised that
It wasn't so bad.

I went to see all the High Schools
And I thought they were cool
But I really do wish that
They all had a swimming pool.

Well, that's what I think of school.

Charlene Galloway (10)
Broughshane Primary School

My Rabbit

My rabbit
Has funny habits,
When I say sit,
He sits.
When I say roll over,
He rolls over.
When I throw a ball,
He would go and fetch it.
And once when we were in the park,
I could have sworn I heard him bark.

Rachel Duffy (10)
Broughshane Primary School

The Star

I saw a star slide down the sky,
Blinding the north as it went by,
Too burning and too quick to hold,
Too lovely to be bought or sold,
Good only to make wishes on,
And then forever to be gone.

Emma Bradley (9)
Broughshane Primary School

AUNTIE ALISTAIR AND UNCLE WILMA

At last, at last, the day has come,
Alistair and Wilma the knot to tie.
There have been many trials along the way,
But Alistair a determined boy was he
Not even chasing by the brush did him deter.
He stuck by Wilma through thick and thin
Carried sticks and bricks,
A nest for to build.
Well I'm short on cousins,
Another soon I'd like,
So when the order in you put,
A boy if you please is all I want.
May God bless you both
As onward together you go.

Ian Mark (11)
Broughshane Primary School

My Poem

There was an old woman in Broughshane,
Who moved to a place called Spain,
She lay in the sun
And ate an icy bun
And now she's driving in pain.

Steven McGall (9)
Broughshane Primary School

MY PET

I have two goldfish
they are called Thunder and Lighting
they swim about the bowl,
my mum feeds them every day.

Darren McAlonan (7)
Broughshane Primary School

THE OLD LADY

There was an old lady
Who lived up a very long lane
She flew up to Spain
In a plane
And never went home again.

Timothy Patton (8)
Broughshane Primary School

SUMMER

Summer is nice and warm
We eat lovely cold ice-lollies
And go to the seaside
And wear our shorts and T-Shirts
Summer Summer Summer

Summer is the time to go
Outside to play
To pick the lovely flowers
The juicy fruit on the trees.

Laura Currie (8)
Broughshane Primary School

My Dog

My dog is furry and plump,
It has a very big bump.
It runs very, very fast,
And sings in a cast.
It has strong legs
And bites my mum's clothes pegs.

Dean Adams (8)
Broughshane Primary School

WINTER IN BROUGHSHANE

Winter in Broughshane
It may be cold
It may be frosty
But winter in Broughshane
Is lovely no matter what

People crying
'Winter's here
Winter's here'
Mothers shouting
'Get your coat on.'

People rushing to shops
To keep warm
Children pulling off their hats and gloves
The minute they reach the shops
Their mothers shouting
'Get your hats and gloves back on.'

Jessica Boal (8)
Broughshane Primary School

VALENTINE'S

V alentine's Day is great
A nd when you have a boy
L ove is floating round
E veryone has presents
N o one is left out.
T ry to keep on going
I n case that love runs out
N o one is sad
E veryone is happy
That boy is for me!

D ay by day I'm leaving
A nd at the end
Y ou're the only one for me.

Jenna Galbraith (10)
Broughshane Primary School

TIGERS

Tigers are sly and mean
their teeth are as sharp as razors
they've very strong legs
to make them speedy.

Chasing deer on the plain
killing and eating
it's what they do
with their teeth.

White and orange ones
with black stripes
camouflage in the grass
the deer stand no chance.

Any predator is in for a surprise
like a leopard or a zebra
is a slap-up meal.

Philip McBurney (11)
Broughshane Primary School

Books

Books are great to read
Whenever you are bored
And you feel the need
To pick up a book and read

Books come in all different shapes
And sizes, exciting, adventure, thriller
Romance and murder, then made into tapes
Books are better than TV, radio and newspapers.

Books can be good, books can be bad
Some can make you feel sad,
Or even mad, mad, *mad*
Books are a bit like this poem

Silly, but good! Silly, but good!
Books put you from a bad mood
To a good one, all in one go
Just go with the flow!

Pick up a book!

Hannah Gibson (11)
Broughshane Primary School

THE NOISE IN THE BASEMENT

There's a noise in the basement!
That I can't understand
Every night when the clock strikes twelve
The noise happens
As if someone is there.

I tell my mum and she thinks I'm mad
I've got to find out what it is!
The next day I told everybody
All my friends laughed and joked.

It was Friday morning and I was getting dressed
When I realised about the noise
I said to myself, I'll go tonight and check it out.

Finally, it's 11.59pm and I better go down now
As I was walking down the stairs to the basement
I thought, what if there's aliens
I kicked open the door to the basement

And there was the noise the *washing machine!*

Josh Boal (11)
Broughshane Primary School

BETTY THE LAMB

I had a little lamb last year
She was so ill and full of fear,
My dad brought her into the house for care
For I to look after under the stair.

Her bed was made of cardboard and straw
She slept all night without a flaw,
To my amazement each morning she woke
To drink her milk mixed with a little yellow egg yoke.

Betty drank her milk through a bottle and teat
The froth ran down her very cheek,
She wagged her tail with such delight
Betty the lamb gained so much might.

Her fleece was white with a few black spots
Her eyes resembled two black dots
Her nose was cute and very small
Her ears pricked up at every call.

Then the day came when Betty went out
Back into the field again
To rejoin her mother strong and stout
I bid her farewell and that was the end.

Patricia Boyd (11)
Broughshane Primary School

HELLO

Hello
Everybody you meet says *Hello,*
But let's say you meet a good old friend and he's in a bad mood
He will not say
Hello

Hello
Let's say you walk down the street, meet your old teacher,
And you didn't really like her,
You would just walk on without saying
Hello

Hello
Let's say you meet a stranger,
Even though you don't know him you still say
Hello

Hello
Let's say you're walking home from school
And you meet your dad and he's in a good mood
Because it's the end of work for the summer holidays
So he says *Hello.*

James Martin (11)
Broughshane Primary School

My Invisible Friend

My invisible friend,
Is always telling jokes,
She's always there to comfort me
When I'm sad and down in the dumps.
Here's some things to tell you,
Just how special she is.

F is for friendly, she always will be,
R is for real, she's not just pretend,
I is for intelligent, she knows everything,
E is for endless, her jokes will never end,
N is for nuisance, she always makes me laugh,
D is for doubtless, she never worries.

Even though you can't see her,
She is still there,
So if you hear someone in your room,
Please don't get scared,
Cause you know it will just be my invisible friend.

Katie Wray (11)
Broughshane Primary School

A Little Dragon

At the corner of my room
A dragon peeped out one day,
It asked me for a glass of water,
So I screamed and ran away.

I heard it crying for attention
So I decided it might not be so bad,
We got on so well together
He was the best friend I ever had!

I named my dragon Pepo
I taught him how to fly,
He took me for great rides on his back
We'll be friends until we die.

Pepo got very old
And caught a terrible illness,
There were no cures for dragons
So he just sat there in stillness.

During the morning
Pepo sadly died,
The memories of Pepo
I'll never leave behind!

Howard Jamieson (11)
Broughshane Primary School

My Dog, Rolo

My dog, Rolo is black,
  Not like a polo,
He's as mad as a hatter
  But I love him no matter.

He gobbles up his food
  It disappears by half,
And when he's in a funny mood
  He always makes me laugh.

He poos and pees
  And my mum boo-hoos,
So I clean it up
  And scold that pup.

I take him for walks
  And have a good talk,
And he acts very good
  Until he's back in the house
And he's as quiet as a mouse!

He's here to stay,
  Although we have to pay
The stress to get him to obey
  But I love him anyway.

Jane Burgess (10)
Broughshane Primary School

SUMMER

Summer is the season for me,
Sandy beaches, warm, hot sun,
Lots of ice cream, deep blue sea,
Going on holidays, oh what fun.

I like going to the swimming pool,
Jumping off the diving board,
Into the water, making me cool,
When I go swimming, I'm never bored.

Going to the park, playing on the swings,
Down the slide onto the ground,
Grazed my elbow, oh, how it stings
Time to go home, have a last look around.

The summer begins to slip away,
How I will miss the warm, hot sun,
I will never forget the summer days,
And how I had so much fun!

Lisa-Jane Millar (11)
Broughshane Primary School

SCHOOL

S is for staff who run this whole place
C is for collage which we do in art
H is for homework which is not much fun
O is for our super school
O is for office where our principal does his work
L is for the lovely surroundings.

Mark Foster (11)
Broughshane Primary School

My N64

I don't know what I'd do without my N64
Playing all those great games like Mario64
When I'm sad it brings me glee and joy
And it's one of my favourite toys.

When I play my Nintendo I have so much fun
I was called for lunch when I made Mario run
Playing Goldeneye and Mario Kart
I'm always pushing some button and start.

I play my Nintendo almost every day
The electric went out, I could no longer play
I could not play my games with a mate
Then I said this isn't so great.

I was demented, mad
And I felt a bit sad
When it came back on, I played a snowboarding game
Anyway I wonder who's to blame?

Nigel Elliott (10)
Broughshane Primary School

My Diabolic Aunts

My diabolic aunts
They're always feeling good,
They're always telling jokes
When I'm in a bad mood.
So here's a few things to tell you
About my diabolic aunts:

M is for manners, that is what they most lack,
Y is for yoghurt, that's their fave food.

D is for diabolic, they are just terrible,
I is for interesting, they've always something to say.
A is for awful, they are so annoying,
B is for Beatrice, that's the older one's name.
O is for odd, they are so weird,
L is for loveable, just because they are.
I is for immature, they are so babyish,
C is for careless, they just do not care!

A is for Audrey - that's her name,
U is for unbearable, well that's what they are.
N is for nuisance, they never go away,
T is for treacherous, they are very dangerous.
S is for special, no one else has aunts like mine!

Christina Magee (11)
Broughshane Primary School

A Dream Motorbike

A man down the street from me
He always wanted a motorbike
It was a Harley Davidson
A dream motorbike!

The problem was he couldn't afford it
The one Harley Davidson he wanted
The only thing he thought about
A dream motorbike!

He played the lottery all the time
He didn't watch television
He thought about the motorbike instead
A dream motorbike!

He was watching the lottery
Just watching the balls
So that he could buy the motorbike
A dream motorbike!

He has a Honda scooter now
But he is desperate for a Harley Davidson
His favourite motorbike the Harley Davidson
A dream motorbike!

But he honestly didn't like it
All that much because it was old
He wanted the Harley Davidson
A dream motorbike!

He was watching the lottery and he won
Thirteen million pounds all his to buy
The Harley Davidson the motorbike!
His dream motorbike!

Gareth McCullough (11)
Broughshane Primary School

Friends

My friends are so good to me
If you met them, you would see
I think they should be on TV
Because they are so good to me

One day I was in a bad mood
But my friends, they still felt good
They took me shopping in the town
And I was no longer with a frown

Then the big day came
And I was no longer the same
I had to transfer to another school
But all my new friends were just as cool!

My new friends took me everywhere
They even took me to see the Mayor!
I cannot believe
All the good friends that I have received

Then we got into a fight
And I got such a fright
But after all, we all joined up
I can't believe I've such good friends.

Keri Smyth (11)
Broughshane Primary School

TIME

1 o'clock, I got hot
2 o'clock, I lost my sock
3 o'clock, I got spots
4 o'clock, I began to say it was a happy day
5 o'clock, they went away
6 o'clock, we bought a tray
7 o'clock, we had a super day
8 o'clock, we sang hip hip hooray
9 o'clock, I went to bed
10 o'clock, I was sleeping, zzzzz
11 o'clock, the house was quiet
12 o'clock, the fireworks went off
That was the end of sleeping.

Iain Loughridge (9)
Broughshane Primary School

Winter For Me

I like winter
Winter is fun
I like to build snowmen
And I love to throw snowballs
And on my snowman's face there is
A carrot for its nose
Some buttons for its eyes
Some sticks for its arms
A hat and some gloves
And of course a mouth.

Cherith O'Hara (7)
Broughshane Primary School

WINTER

Winter is here
A boy is wearing winter clothes
It is cold in winter
People start to make snowmen.

They throw snowballs
Winter is fun
Car engines stall
People get cross.

Peter Thompson (7)
Broughshane Primary School

WINTER

Winter is snow
Fun is in winter
Out I go into the snow
Out into the shivering cold

I make a snowman
With eyes that never close
When morn comes he's melted
All that's left is his scarf.

Jenny McCandless (7)
Broughshane Primary School

WINTER IS HERE

Winter is coming
It is exciting
We put the Christmas tree up
It is only six days.

I got a book
The Christmas dinner was great
I love Christmas
We made a snowman.

Ciara Topping (7)
Broughshane Primary School

WINTER

I love winter
I like making a snowman
I like throwing snowballs
Animals hibernating in winter
We shiver in winter
Winter is freezing cold
The days are shorter.

David Murray (7)
Broughshane Primary School

WINTER IS HERE

Winter is wonderful
Kids enjoy it
It snows a lot
I love to feel it
I love to throw snowballs
The car won't go, it is frozen
It is bitter
There are icy roads
Winter is wonderful.

Christopher Smyth (7)
Broughshane Primary School

WINTER TO ME

I like winter
Winter is fun
I like to make a snowman
The trees are bare
I wear a hat and a scarf
Winter is a time to be happy
The duck pond is frozen
The ducks are cold.

Nicole Connor (7)
Broughshane Primary School

WINTER

Winter's freezing cold
We shiver in the cold
We build a snowman
With buttons made of coal
A carrot nose
A hat on his head
The days are shorter.

Chloe Kennedy (7)
Broughshane Primary School

WINTER FUN

The wind blows
The children scream
The cars' engines squeak
Christmas trees are up
People sing carols
It is my favourite month
People make Christmas things.

David Nelson (6)
Broughshane Primary School

Through A Child's Eyes

When I was
A little girl,
My eyes were
Blue as the sky,
My cheeks were
Red as roses,
My love was way up high.
Now when I see a rainbow
I think of the sky, sky, sky.

Gemma Lindsay (8)
Broughshane Primary School

Books

Books are good
Books are fun
Books are for everyone

Books can be a treat
Books you can't eat
Books can test your brain

Books can be tall
Books can be small
Books are for all

Books can be sad
Books can be bad
Books can make you glad.

Julie-Anne Cairns (11)
Broughshane Primary School

A Friend

Everybody needs a friend,
Someone on whom you can depend,
Everyone needs a friend,
And they will be there till the end.

A friend is someone you know will be there,
Someone who will always care,
A friend helps you in the toughest times,
Even if you have committed crimes.

A friend is someone who will give you support,
And play together in sport,
A good friend will never leave you,
And sometimes they will need you.

Mark McNeill (10)
Broughshane Primary School

Winter

When winter snow falls,
We wrap up warm,
Hats, scarves, gloves, coats and welly boots,
It's so much fun.

When I walk in the crisp white snow you hear,
Crackle, crunch, crackle,
We build snowmen,
Have snowball fights
And ride on our toboggans.

Birds come fluttering down,
To eat all the goodies,
Icicles shine in the sunlight,
Like diamonds in the air.

Fires blazing all day long,
Hot toast cooking,
As the cat lies curled up sleeping in front
Of the blazing fire.

Kathryn Thompson (10)
Broughshane Primary School

Farm Day

I went to the farm,
Next to the barn,
To get some hay and corn,
Then to the kitchen,
To fry an egg
And see the new-born lamb.

I heard the sound of the tractor splutter
And then I heard the farmer mutter,
'Drat, it's done it again,'
The farmer was cross,
He jumped from the cab,
Right into the muck,
His wellies stuck!

It's Friday the thirteenth,
His dear wife said,
'If you'd listened to me
You'd have stayed in your bed!
So just sit yourself down
And I'll make some tea.

Tomorrow's another day!'

Peter Gilmore (9)
Broughshane Primary School

Pop Groups

S Club 7 are the best,
better than all the rest.
Storming at number 1 with 'Reach'
their voices will just never screech.

Britney Spears being stronger,
her song videos should be longer.
Her hairstyles are good,
she could make her songs more exciting if she could.

There are many pop groups like
Jennifer Lopez, Steps, Westlife,
Alice Deejay, Emimen, Craig David,
Vengaboys, these are some song
artists I like.

Cathryn Maybin (11)
Broughshane Primary School

THE HAUNTED HOUSE

Creeping quietly as a mouse,
I entered the haunted house,
As I tiptoed up the stairs,
Someone called out 'Beware!'

I ran down the stairs
And out of the door,
I just couldn't take it anymore,
That was the last of the haunted house.

Cara Faith (9)
Broughshane Primary School

MONTHS OF THE YEAR

January brings celebrations of the New Year
February brings hugs and kisses
March brings the spring; all birds sing
April brings big chocolate eggs
May brings May Day
June brings summer
July brings lollipops
August brings bank holiday
September brings back to school
October brings ghosts and witches
November brings the gun powder plot
December brings snow and Santa.

Katrina Douglas (9)
Broughshane Primary School

Doctor, Doctor

The doctor called me pale face
And then looked down my throat
And to my chest he listened
With a stethoscope
I coughed and coughed until my throat was sore
The doctor gave me medicine
And then I coughed no more
Back again the following week
But still not feeling at my peak
Doctor checked me once again
And I told him of my pain
My right side it is so sore
I feel like squealing in an uproar
Appendicitis it must be
Surgery, I'm afraid, said he
Then to the hospital I had to go
My knees wobbling to and fro
Doctor said 'Don't worry it'll soon be by'
Then I woke up propped up in bed
Looking around with a rather light head
I was so glad I had not died
Mum and Dad at the bedside
So that's the end of my tale
And now my face is not quite so pale.

Ashley McCandless (10)
Broughshane Primary School

Horrible School

School is boring,
Without any fun,
But it is better when the work's all done.

We have a nice teacher,
But she is very cross,
She makes us work all day long.

Our classroom stinks,
The tables rot,
The glass is braking
And the floor is rotten.

When the teacher is not looking,
We mess about,
Jump on the tables,
When the windows are open we throw things out.

We run down the corridor towards the hall,
We manage to make a mess of the wall,
And then we kick the doors down.

When it's time to go home,
I say
'What a horrible day.'

Christopher McClean (10)
Broughshane Primary School

SEASONS

In the winter the snow will fall
We usually hear the children call
In the springtime when it's May
The little lambs start to play
In the summer it gets really hot
And we get sunburn quite a lot
When in autumn the leaves start to die
As we all mostly sigh
Now it's back to winter, it's another year
When we think back, there's a little tear.

Emma Graham (10)
Broughshane Primary School

WINTER

W is for winter which is very cold
I is for igloo that I built last year
N is for nuts in some Christmas puddings
T is for turkey which we have on Christmas Day
E is for excitement when the first snow comes
R is for reindeer that pulls Santa's sleigh.

Philip Smyth (9)
Broughshane Primary School

School

Work, work, work, work,
Is the teacher's middle name,
I wish I could get out of here, it's full of awful shame.
Should I ask the caretaker,
Should I ask my mum,
Why is it me that has to be so dumb?
Should I climb out of the window,
Or just walk out the door,
Or maybe freefall through the floor.
Maybe I could launch a rocket into space,
At least I could get out of this boring place.

No it's the weekend,
Time to relax by the pool,
I hope I don't go back
To that awful place called school.

Grant Campbell (10)
Broughshane Primary School

My Cat

My cat
likes eating rats,
especially fat and juicy ones.
Ones with short tails even count,
gulp, 1, 2, 3.

My cat
likes eating bats,
ones with black curly wings.
The only thing left is the eyes,
gulp, 1, 2, 3.

My cat
likes eating birds,
birds have nice sweet juicy breasts.
Ones that are small even count,
gulp, 1, 2, 3.

My cat
loves eating rats, bats and birds.
Gulp, 1, 2, 3,
that's them all eaten.

Tanya Wilson (10)
Broughshane Primary School

GHOST HOUSE

In the middle of Ghost House,
Across the floor scampered a mouse.
Its little feet scrape the floor,
Soon its paws got very sore.

It stopped and rested under a chair,
No idea it was going to get a scare.
The ghost floated out from the dark,
For its nightmare stock.

The little mouse shrieked with fear,
When the ghost turned to peer.
The little mouse ran with fright,
Until the ghost was nowhere in sight.

David Evans (8)
Broughshane Primary School

Her Eyes

Her eyes turned yellow
I think she wanted to meet a jolly good fellow.
Her eyes turned pink
I think she wanted to go to an ice rink.
Her eyes turned red
I think she wanted some bread.
Her eyes turned white
I think she saw quite a good sight.
Her eyes turned grey
I think she was planning to run away.
Her eyes turned brown
I think she is going to have a big frown.
Her eyes turned dazzling blue
I think she got caught in some sticky glue.
Now my poem has come to an end
And I've introduced you to my very best friend.

Steven Mairs (9)
Broughshane Primary School

WINTER

Winter is just around the corner,
I loved the white snow,
It was very good to throw.
I loved my snowman,
I had great fun,
Then the snow went away,
My cousins came up to play.

Nicole Bradley (7)
Broughshane Primary School

WINTER

Winter is very cold
I like to see falling snow
Down from the sky
It is very white
Very crunchy too
I like snow
It's fun to play with
Birds are very hungry
They cannot find food.

Michelle Finlay (6)
Broughshane Primary School

WINTER

Winter is very cold,
It makes me shiver,
The snow is very pretty,
The birds are very hungry.
When I want to go out,
I have to put on my winter clothes.
If you are good,
Santa Claus will come,
He'll give you lots of presents.

Christine Maybin (7)
Broughshane Primary School

Winter

When we get up in the morning
It is cold and icy
We go skating on the frozen pond
We like it when it is winter
Santa only comes to good
Children.

Kathryn O'Hara (7)
Broughshane Primary School

Winter

Jack Frost is about
He is very cold
You have to wrap up
Nice and warm
Or else you will catch the cold
In winter it is Christmas
Santa is going to come
Only if you are good.

Evie Carrington (6)
Broughshane Primary School

Winter

Winter is a great surprise
Even if it's cold
If you sit by the fire
You will be nice and warm
It is cosy on the sofa
It's nice snuggled in front of the fire.

Andrew Duffy (7)
Broughshane Primary School

WEATHER

The bed of clouds hurries past.
They moved across the sea of sky.
The sheets of rain came pouring down
And the wall of wind blew us about.
Then a sun of fire warmed us up.

Jason Paul (8)
Broughshane Primary School

WEATHER

The sun is a golden ball
That rules over the sky
The rain is a falling star
That falls onto Earth
The fog is a visible ghost
That comes out in the morning
The snow is a white sheet
That covers up the Earth
The clouds are giant planes
That hover above me and you
The wind is an invisible creature
That flies in our faces.

Jill Robinson (9)
Broughshane Primary School

POEM

Slippey, slidey, lots of fun,
Just like eating a Christmas bun.
Icy, spicy, button on toast,
Just like eating Christmas roast.
Screeching fire, lovely and warm,
People come in great form.
Now heading to bed with a sleepy head,
Santa comes with lots of toys,
Hearing of all the good girls and boys.

Rachel Harkness (9)
Broughshane Primary School

Winter

Snow and ice
We love to play
On an icy day
Skating and sliding
And sledge riding
It's slippery and cold
Just remember don't be bare
We have to get wrapped up
In warm clothes
And then put heavy boots
Over our toes
Then go out and enjoy the fun
And sometime later out comes the sun.

Jack Burgess (8)
Broughshane Primary School

FISHY

Swimming across the sea,
Must be very tiring,
Long days looking for something to eat,
But if you were me,
You would be fed,
Sleeping the day away,
Snoring your head away,
Your bubbles going, *pop, pop, pop.*

Amy Coleman (9)
Broughshane Primary School

RAIN

Wind and rain
is such a pain,
sleet and snow
worse again,
tucked up warm in my bed,
listen to it patter on the
garden shed,
rain is bad,
wind is sad,
when it goes away,
I am very glad.

Jodie Calderwood (9)
Broughshane Primary School

The Harvest Table

On the harvest table,
There are lots of juicy apples,
And some gooey red stuff,
Some orange things like football.

There are silly yellow things,
Round, juicy things,
Lovely pink flowers,
And lots more.

But sometimes I wonder
Why they are there,
And I always remember,
Harvest is here!

Rachel Mairs (7)
Broughshane Primary School

The Goggly

The Goggly has orange hair
And blue eyes as well.
It has a purple snout,
It is three foot tall
But that's not all!

He has dark red claws
And 14 paws!
A whiplash tail,
A green, green mouth,
But that's not all!

At night he goes hunting
For mice with rice,
That's his favourite.
When the Goggly goes to sleep,
Not a sound is heard.

Kathryn Hamilton (7)
Broughshane Primary School

THE FLYING KITE

Under the world
And over the sky
Fly a kite
The colours so bright.
Up very high
You'll see the sky
So very bright.

Laura Finlay (8)
Broughshane Primary School

The Kitten

The little kitten sits
Under the sun
To sleep all day
And have lots of fun.
It plays with the wool
And is a fool
It jumps about
Until it's time to sleep.

Catherine Chambers (7)
Broughshane Primary School

WINTER

W is for the winter days
I is for the icicles that hang
N is for the nippy mornings
T is for the turning cold
E is for the elephants that skid
R is for the people that ride in the cold.

Janine Mark (7)
Broughshane Primary School

Germs

I'm sick and I'm in bed
I have a sore head.
Oh doctor please come quick!
Or I'll die in bed.

Kathryn Gilmore (8)
Broughshane Primary School

Ill

I'm sick, I'm in bed
My tummy's sore and so's my head.
I should have looked what was on my plate
And paid attention to what I ate.

Hannah McCooke (7)
Broughshane Primary School

HORSES

H orses are practically the same as ponies
O nly, horses are over 14.2h.h - ponies below.
R iders wear hard hats to
S top them hurting their heads. Nearly
E very rider wears one of these hats, and I think those who don't
S hould.

Joanne Fleck (11)
Moorfields Primary School

FOOTBALL

F ouling going
O n
O ut
T here on the pitch, all going after the
B all. Everyone wants to show their skill
A nd try to score a goal.
L obbing the keeper, the crowd
L ove it all.

Brian McCartney (10)
Moorfields Primary School

The Year Two Thousand

T he years two thousand was exciting for everyone
H eroes and film stars brought out their biggest films ever
E ven my dad was getting excited

Y oung people were jumping up and down with glasses of coke
E verything had limited edition on it
A man claimed he saw Jesus but nobody knows
R eally I thought it was brilliant

T wo other people said they could fly
W ell anyway by this point we are getting our party poppers ready
O h and my cousin forgot his glass

T wo, one and just then he comes running in, Happy New Year
H ouses everywhere were partying all night
O verseas people are partying
U ndivided attention was everywhere
S un rises and Mum is making a fry-up
A nd everybody is very hungry
N obody talks until they've finished
D enver got up last as usual but all in all it was very good!

Richard Campbell (10)
Moorfields Primary School

FOOTBALL

F ootball is my favourite sport
O h the best sport of all
O n the muddy pitch
T rying my very best
B lasting the ball sky-high
A iming for the net
L ots of screaming fans
L ooking for that winning goal!

Philip Houston (10)
Moorfields Primary School

The Afternoon Walk

When Debbie and I go out for a walk,
We hold each other's hand and talk
Of all the things we mean to do
When Debbie and I are twenty-two.

When we've thought about a thing,
Like bowling hoops or cycling,
Or playing with Debbie's balloon,
We do it all in the afternoon.

Emma Ayre (11)
Moorfields Primary School

SCHOOL

S chool again, for another day,
C lass is fun, at times
H ome again
O h! This feels good
O h! Not another day
L azy, slow, Monday morning again.

Zoë Moore (11)
Moorfields Primary School

Breakfast At Moorfields

The birds on the wire,
Look down and enquire,
'How long till they all go away?'
'Don't know,' said the crow,
'But they'll all have to go,
They can't stay out here all day.'

'Mrs Scott is not happy,
With that P7 chappie,
She says he's a bully, no doubt.
He steals P1's lunches,
And pulls the girls' bunches,
And swears, and sticks his tongue out.'

'Oh, I hear the bell,
I know that sound well,'
Said the little red robin called Joe.
'They'll be gone in a flash,
Then we'll make a dash
For our breakfast spread out down below.'

'There's biscuits and buns,
And crisps by the tons,
So much for the 'No Litter' sign.
We'll eat till we're full,
This place is *so* cool,
See you tomorrow, same time!'

Hayley McKeown (11)
Moorfields Primary School

A Typical Day

Oh goodness gracious me
Come take a look at my family
I've got a sister, three brothers, a mum and a dad
And they all make me extremely mad.
In the morning Mum calls, 'Get up, get up!'
There's cereal in the bowl and there's tea in the cup.
At school I have maths, English and PE
Oh dear, my teacher is shouting at me!
Time to go home and have my tea,
My homework is all done and it's time for TV.
Oh no, it's nearly ten o'clock; it's nearly time for bed,
'Get up those stairs Aaron!' that's what my mum said.

Aaron McAuley (11)
Moorfields Primary School

Mum

Mum thinks she's boss,
But I don't give a toss,
She says tidy my room,
And sweep up with the broom,
I hoover the house,
Then feed the pet mouse,
I'm like her gofer,
When I hear her say 'Go fetch my lofer,'
She says wash the dishes,
And I can only make wishes,
That she would stop
And go pop
And come back as *my* slave.

Louise Cooper (11)
Moorfields Primary School

Crazy Cars

Some cars are fast
Some cars are slow,
But all of the cars
Have somewhere to go.

Some cars are big
Some cars are small,
But my big Ferrari
Is the biggest of all.

Some cars are red
Some cars are blue,
But you will know my Ferrari
When I whiz past you.

Andrew Munce (11)
Moorfields Primary School

How To Write A Poem

I don't know much about poetry
I don't know how to write it
But the one thing I do know
Is that you do it, bit by bit.

You start off with the title
Then you do the first line
You do the rest of the verse
But it may not have to rhyme.

The poem can be an adventure
Thrilling, love or true
But one thing you have to remember
Is that it's all up to you.

Craig McCullough (10)
Moorfields Primary School

MY BEST FRIEND

When I was a boy,
And my dog was a pup,
Through the fields we'd stray
Just a boy and his dog.
We had such great fun,
We grew up together that way.

I remember the time at the old riverbank
When I could have drowned without doubt,
But my dog was there to the rescue he came,
He jumped in and pulled me out.

As time did unfold
My dog he grew old,
He quickly became very ill,
And now I'm alone to play by myself,
I miss my best pal still.

My dog he has gone
Where all dogs go,
No more by my side will he roam,
If there is a dog heaven then I know
That is my best friend's 'new home'.

Steven McCammond (11)
Moorfields Primary School

My Home

Here at my home Tannybrake
There's lots to do each day,
Helping Dad on the farm
As well as games to play.

Feeding and milking the cows,
Now I like doing that,
But Skippy and Speckles the calves
Keep licking my fingers and hat.

Suzy the small pony
Is much too fat,
More exercise, less grass
She'll not like that.

Kerryhill sheep are all indoors,
As lambing time is near,
Shows and young handler classes
To go to each year.

Patch the old dog
Carries my shoes to his bed,
While Sam the young collie
Prefers to chew sticks instead.

Sooty my big black cat
He catches birds and mice,
But Lucy the tortoiseshell lady
Lies by the fire so pretty and nice.

Life on the farm
Is busy all year through,
For animals, pets and people
Have all so much to do.

Ruth Barr (11)
Moorfields Primary School

MONKEYS AT PLAY!

Looking at the treetops,
Way up in the sky.
That's where you see them swing,
Up on high!

Tempt them with bananas,
Tempt them with fruit.
They will appear from everywhere,
From the treetops to the roots.

So small and so furry,
But yet they eat in a hurry,
Sometimes they make me laugh
With their funny little ways!

Deborah Fleck (11)
Moorfields Primary School

Books

Thin books, thick books,
colourful books, dull books.
Big books, small books,
tall books, middle-sized books.

Non-fiction books, fiction books,
scary books, adventure books,
science fiction books, fact books.
Ah, the library is the place for me!

Philip Moffett (10)
Moorfields Primary School

In A Minute . . .

I can count to one hundred there and back,
I can put potatoes in a sack.
I can make a milkshake,
I can help my mum to bake.
I can play football,
I can walk to and from the hall.
I can pack my bag for school,
I can think of having fun in the pool.
I can make a paper aeroplane,
I can build a Lego toy crane.
I can set the table for having tea,
I can phone my friend or maybe he'll phone me.
What can you do in one minute?

Ryan Kerr (10)
Moorfields Primary School

TEACHERS

T eachers teach me lots of things
E very day at school
A nd when it comes to science it
C an brighten up my day.
H elp is what I need sometimes with
E nglish and my maths
R ight or wrong, I'll try my best
S o I'll get good results.

David Fleck (11)
Moorfields Primary School

Free Kick

He stepped up to take the free kick
And smacked the ball right on the side
It was like the sun flying through the sky
This would decide who would go through
And the keeper was like the moon
Ready for the sun to go down
But they had scored and the sun
Would shine another day.

David Campbell (11)
Moorfields Primary School

HOLIDAYS

H olidays are lots of fun
O nly if there's lots of things to do
L ovely days and -
I n and out of the swimming pool
D own by the beach, oh what fun
A s the days go drifting by
Y ellow sand and blue sea
S ome people think holidays are bad, but I don't.

Emma Cameron (11)
Moorfields Primary School

The Birds At The Quarry

The birds at the quarry
Sat down to worry
About the men in the lorry
Who came to say sorry
They thought they would get shot
And put in a pot
It would be hot
And that would be the end of the lot!
Anyway, they flew away
When all the lorry men wanted to say
Was hey!
Come and play on Saturday!

Anna Caldwell (11)
Moorfields Primary School

THE FAMINE

An empty stomach
Hunger lurking everywhere
No yellow cornmeal.

No bag of oatmeal
Only small potato skins,
Not a lot to eat.

Lucy McLaughlin (10)
St Mary's Primary School

The Great Redwood

The redwood against my skin
As the wind whistles through the gentle hollow
The red glow of the sun
Shines in my eyes.
As turtle doves fly over and some magpies
And if you listen
You'll hear the music play
As leprechauns dance
In the yellow hay.

Johnnie McKillop (11)
St Mary's Primary School

Dog And Cat

The cat sat on the mat
He loved to do just that
The dog came in looking gloom
And ending the cat groom
The cat sprang from his mat
Spat at the dog and said, 'Take that!'
The dog ran from the room
Then came back quite soon
'Mr Cat, you can't do that
It's not only your mat.'
Mum heard this out in the yard
Came running in quite hard
'Get out, the pair of yous.
Wait! Who tore my shoes?'
The dog looked at the cat
'I'm not taking the blame for that.'
'Meow,' said the cat, 'Me too.
We're not buying any new shoes.'
Now they're the best of friends
This is how my poem ends.

Carmel McCambridge (8)
St Mary's Primary School

My First Pet

Oh what shall my first pet be?
Shall it be a cat, a dog or even an elephant?
Could it be a mouse to scare people out of the house?
Oh what shall I get for a pet?
Would I get a tarantula?
Oh what a sight would I see, my mum, oh no.
Oh I may get a zebra or even a lion or a cheetah.
A fish would do nicely for a pet but all it does is swim.
The best pet is me.
So says my mum.

Patrick McLaughlin (9)
St Mary's Primary School

MATH POEM

A is for add which all of us do.
B is for bigger that add makes it too.
C is for counting 1, 2, 3, 4, 5.
D is for division and that means divide.
E is for even and we don't mean flat.
F is for fraction, how about that?
G is for good, the teacher writes on my book.
H is for one hundred, take a look.
I is for the ink blot I get on my page.
J is for joy, teacher's not in a rage.
K is for kite, a four-sided shape.
L is for long division, I hope I escape!
M is for maths, which I enjoy.
N is for numbers for Mrs Molloy.
O is for odd which some numbers are.
P is for percentage, we haven't done so far.
Q is for a question teacher might ask.
R is for right answer, what a very hard task!
S is for six which comes before seven.
T is for ten, one more is eleven.
U is for untidy, we must keep our sums neat.
V is for very good if we manage the feat.
W is for winner who completed the yellow card.
X is for 'multiply', these can be quite hard.
Y is for yawn, all the numbers in my head.
Z is for zzzz, it's time I was in bed.

Ann Burke (8)
St Mary's Primary School

THE POWERFUL FLOUR BAG

I own a great big factory,
And it's run by . . . guess who? Me!
One day someone tapped me on the back,
And said, 'Hey! Is that cake-making lack?'

I was so horrified, that I spun right round,
I saw no-one there,
So, my heart began to pound.

I thought, for a moment,
Was that, that bag of flour?
But then, I said 'Ah! No!
It would have to have special power!
But, little did I know,
It was the flour,
Oh help! Oh no!

I found this out,
A bit later on,
When I was looking for the flour,
And I found it was gone!
Oh no! I thought,
It does have power!
The kind that makes people shower,
All day long, 'til they bloom a flower!
Oh no! I thought, I'll lose my job!
Soon, a man came in, a big ugly snob,
He bought the factory,
From me.
And yes, I did lose my job!

Niamh Horscroft (8)
St Mary's Primary School

The Day That The Witch Met David Beckham

There was once a very old witch,
Who liked to play on the football pitch.
She met David Beckham,
But she wanted to kick him,
So he threw her in a very deep ditch!

Jordan Delaney (9)
St Mary's Primary School

THE OLD MAN FROM WALES

There was an old man from Wales
Who loved to steal at the sales.
He was caught by a cop,
Who told him to stop,
But he escaped in a van filled with bales.

Paul Smart (9)
St Mary's Primary School

THE OLD MAN

There was a very old man
Who ran all the way to Japan
He thought he was clever
But his brain was a feather
But his favourite food was jam.

Matthew Bowen (9)
St Mary's Primary School

Wee Jerry

There was a young man called Jerry,
He came from a place called Kerry.
He went to school,
Played with some wool,
And now his face is all hairy.

Rita O'Neill (9)
St Mary's Primary School

THERE ONCE WAS A MAN FROM SAN FRANCISCO

There once was a man from San Francisco
Whose speed when driving was slow
He went to Spar
Won a new car
And now you should see him go!

Eamon O'Neill (10)
St Mary's Primary School

THE OLD MAN FROM AYR

There was an old man from Ayr,
Who tried to let off a flare,
It went the wrong way,
Then he ran away,
And he ended up in intensive care.

Mark Donaghy (9)
St Mary's Primary School

THE MAN CALLED SCOOTER

There once was a man named Scooter
Who jammed six white rats up his hooter
He did it for a bet
With the money he'll get
He'll be able to buy a computer.

Stephen Donaghy (9)
St Mary's Primary School

ANNA

There was a girl named Anna,
Her favourite food was banana,
She ate about ten,
Then she ate a hen,
And for supper she ate her pet llama.

Maria McAllister (9)
St Mary's Primary School

The Man Called Stan

There once lived a man called Stan,
Who was a really funny man,
He drank all the beer,
That was for the New Year
And was chased far away to Japan.

Seamus McNaughton (9)
St Mary's Primary School

THE MAN FROM SPAIN

There once was a man from Spain,
Who just hated eating chow mein,
Though he was Spanish,
Suddenly he vanished,
To tell you the truth, he wasn't very sane!

Alison McKeggan (10)
St Mary's Primary School

The Inventor Of Gin!

There was a young man who invented gin,
While making it he made a terrible din,
It tasted quite nice,
And had a great price,
But most of it was put in the bin!

Ciara Frances McAllister (10)
St Mary's Primary School

The Woman On Top Of The Hill

There was an old woman called Jill,
Who lived on top of a hill.
Her feet were so sore,
And her head even more,
That she went to Dr Al for a pill.

Aidan McNaughton (9)
St Mary's Primary School

The Young Man From Cork

There was a young man from Cork,
Who really wanted to go to York,
So he went on the boat,
And it began to float,
Until the boat got burst by a fork.

Patricia J McNaughton (9)
St Mary's Primary School

Bill

There was a man called Bill,
He sat on a window sill,
He drank some beer,
At the end of the year,
And changed his name to Phil.

Joanne Stewart (10)
St Mary's Primary School

JACK

There was a man called Jack
Who carried a very heavy sack.
He carried it up a hill
And stopped at the mill
Because he got a terrible sore back.

Ciara-Helen McAllister (10)
St Mary's Primary School

A Girl Called Ann

There once was a young girl called Ann,
Who knocked herself out with a pan,
Her head was so sore,
There was a knock at the door,
And it was her best friend called Jan.

Mary McAteer (10)
St Mary's Primary School

THE BOY FROM TURKEY

There was a boy from Turkey
Who ate some chicken curry
He took a drink from the sink
And had to go in a hurry!

Aoife Quinn (9)
St Mary's Primary School

Silly Ping

There was an old man called Ping
Who asked a girl for a ring
He dropped it and it broke
He thought it was a joke
But the girl, for him would not sing.

Jessica Gillan (9)
St Mary's Primary School

CUSHENDALL

Deep in the Glens,
There is a place I love to be,
My own hometown,
Is the only place for me.

I'll stay here forever,
Never will I move away,
This place is special,
In every kind of way.

I'm never on my own,
There are people all around,
There might not be a lot to do,
But this is a wonderful place I've found.

Rough, green everywhere,
Mountains big and high,
A small seaside village,
With the sea reaching out to touch the sky.
How I love Cushendall.

Fiona McAlister (11)
St Mary's Primary School

My Little Sister

My little sister is weird
I think that she is an alien
Her fringe covers her two eyes

My little sister is so sick
Mammy took her temperature
She scooped back her fringe
And guess what she saw?

Another two eyes!

Emma Duignan (9)
St Mary's Primary School

School Is Weird

My school is weird
The children too
We do *nothing*
No subjects
Not one

We go back in classroom
The teacher was
Dressed in very odd clothes
I won't mention her name
She'll look me in the eye

We have no
Dinners
No *nothing*
I'll starve

I hope the 'next' school is
Sooooo much better and
I hope the teacher wears
A sweater.

Ciara Campbell (9)
St Mary's Primary School

Let's Look Into The Future

Wouldn't it be just great
To look into the future.
We might have invented
Hovercrafts that float
Without petrol or diesel.
Maybe we could have time machines
To go even further into time.
We could have virtual reality helmets.
Children might be allowed to
Use bazookas or M60s and
Other dangerous guns.
We could have robot servants
That feed us.

Just imagine!

Michael Kane (9)
St Mary's Primary School

My First Day At School

On my first day at school
Everyone thought it was cool!
I think they're wrong
Because it's not.
We did a *lot* of work.
I felt like a jerk.
When it was break ~ And
I got a bit of cake!
When it was hometime
I said, *'At last!'*
And I ran out the door
In a blast.

Kathryn McAlister (9)
St Mary's Primary School

The Best Sweetie Shop!

Raspberry truffle,
Ice-cream with flakes,
King-sized Mars bars,
And cherry cakes!

Little children flooding in,
Hoping that,
They will win,
First place in the best,
Sweetie shop queue.

I would like to,
Be there now,
Sure,
Wouldn't you?
With lots of sweets,
To suck and chew!

There's little ice lollies,
And pretend iced hollies,
All in the,
Best sweetie shop,
In town.

Jane Molloy (9)
St Mary's Primary School

ART

A is for art teacher who teaches you art.
R is for Rachel who can paint good pictures.
T is for tips that help us out.
I is for Irene who is my art teacher.
S is for scribbles which babies do.
T is for technology which I *love!*

Anne-Marie Fleet (9)
St Mary's Primary School

LOVING

L is for love, tender and care
O is for others that love you so
V is for very giving and very nice
I is for icing on top of our cake
N is for next, buying clothes for your wife
G is for giving an engagement ring.

Caolan Carson (8)
St Mary's Primary School

A Wonderful Day At The Beach

A wonderful day at the beach it was,
We splashed, we splished and we sploshed,
Until it started to rain,
When we got home,
I just went for a bath,
When we were dressed again,
It had stopped raining
So off to the beach we went,
We splashed, we splished and sploshed.

Oh what a day at the beach, it was.

Alexandra McLaughlin (9)
St Mary's Primary School

My Pen

This is the pen that I write with all day,
This is the pen that I got on Tuesday.

This is the pen with a fluffy end,
This is the pen that can bend.

This is the pen that has yellow, blue and red,
This is the pen that I take to bed.

This is the pen with the rubber at the end,
This is the pen that I would never give or lend.

This is the pen that I have never met,
This is the pen I will never forget.

Tessa McDonnell (9)
St Mary's Primary School

I HAVE A LITTLE BROTHER!

I have a little brother
He is a little rat
He dances round the house all night
And scares the blooming cat

He races on the scooter
He races up and down
He always tries to scare himself
Until his pants go brown

He has a dirty habit
He picks his nose all night
I wish he wouldn't do it
For it's such a sickening sight!

Bronagh Heggarty (9)
St Mary's Primary School

Sounds

I don't like the sound of rattling milk bottles. Clang! Clang!
I don't like the sound of people screaming. Eeeaat! Eeeaat!
Do you like the sound of children shouting? I don't.
I don't like the sound of milk bottles breaking. Smash! Smash!
I don't like the sound of the fire crackling in the fireplace.
Now I do like the sound of cars rallying out. Errr! Errr!
And I do like the sound of motorbikes skidding around the track.
I like the sound of the TV chatting and chatting away.
And I do like the radio speaking through the speakers.
I like the sound of people tap dancing. Tap! Tap! Tap!

Brian McMullan (8)
St Patrick's Primary School

SILENCE

Listen!
Can you hear?
The sound of a rabbit sniffing as it hops by,
The sound of a pencil writing letters as it goes.
Can you hear the sound of a rubber dropping on the ground?
Can you hear the water in the pipes as it rushes to the tap?
Can you hear the sound of a jet, flying place to place?
Can you hear the sound of a watch ticking away through the day?
Can you hear the sound of the spiders creeping through the grass?

Catriona McLean (8)
St Patrick's Primary School

SILENCE

Silence is when you can hear things.
Listen!
Can you hear?
clouds flowing in the sky,
birds landing on earth,
chalk moving on the blackboard.

Listen!
Can you hear?
Children painting a picture,
or a lion hiding in the bushes,
now listen,
listen to silent sounds you can hear.

Emma McKean (9)
St Patrick's Primary School

SILENCE

Listen!
Can you hear?
The clouds moving and disappearing in the sky.
The birds flying past the windows.
The bees sucking honey.
The crabs creeping in the sand.
The snakes slithering on the grass.

The aeroplanes flying way up in the sky.
The farmers walking on the grass.
A person's heart beating.

Francis O'Neill (9)
St Patrick's Primary School

SOUNDS

Listen! Listen! Listen to the sounds, East, West, South and North.
Sounds! Sounds! Sounds in a park where there are children.
If you have a motorbike listen to its sound.
Let it go, burn rubber, listen to its sound.
If you go to a football match and your team has lost.
You will leave without a sound.
But the other teams fans
Will leave with the biggest
Sound!

Connor McGilligan (8)
St Patrick's Primary School

Silence

Listen
Can you hear?
The fish gently swim through the sea,
The boats sailing across the sea,
All of the people breathing,
The sun coming up,
When people whisper to you,
People walking on the floor,
The flies flying by,
People when they touch each other,
When your hair moves from side to side.

Celine O'Kane (8)
St Patrick's Primary School

SILENCE

Listen!
Can you hear?
A cat scampering around the floor,
Or someone whispering in a low, low voice,
Birds swooping past the window.

Can you hear?
A flower growing in the garden,
The trees swaying in the wind,
Spiders climbing up a tree.

Can you hear?
Dogs jumping through the long grass,
People getting older each day,
Crooks tiptoe across the yard.
Can you hear?

Jezamine Pressly (8)
St Patrick's Primary School

Silence

Listen!
Can you hear?
Your heart beating every single day of your life.
The silent sound of people breathing.
The low ticking of the clock.
The soft snowflakes fall at your feet.
The wind whistling when you are inside.
The baby birds hatching every spring.
The flowers growing as summer comes.

Rosemarie McKeown (8)
St Patrick's Primary School

Advice To Gran

Why don't you go out
And enjoy yourself Gran?
Why not try crisps or chocolate
And throw away your old frying pan?
Have some fun on a shopping trip.
Jump the queue
But please don't slip!
Get some new TV channels
With digital sky
And wave your cleaning
Goodbye!

Conor McMullan (11)
St Patrick's Primary School

COLOURS

Colours are cool
Colours are bright
I see them each day
I see them each night
The grass is green
The sky is blue
All life is varied in colour
The way God meant it to be.
If everyone would stop and think
Please not quarrel
Please not fight
Let our true colours shine
Don't take the colour out of life
What do you think?

Bridget McGinty (11)
St Patrick's Primary School

I'M ANGRY

Teeth grinding
Blood boiling
Hair curling . . .
    I'm Angry

Brow sweating
Hands shaking
Knees knocking . . .
    I'm Angry

Body shaking
Heart thumping
Eyes open . . .
    I'm only dreaming.

Catherine McGarry (11)
St Patrick's Primary School

Our Experience At Midnight

12.00 midnight draws near,
The castle is silent,
We're watching here,
Suddenly we hear a sound,
Don't worry . . .
It's just a mouse running across the room.

Hearts are pounding,
Tension mounting,
We all hold hands saying slowly,
'Come out, ghost, we're ready now.'
After that we hear a boom!

Out he comes with a *Boo!*
'If you don't get out I'll kill all of you!'
We didn't move, not one inch,
So scared,
So threatened,
We had to pinch,
Then suddenly my friend, Maura
Takes a flash and sends him roaring!

We all knew that was our token . . .
To leave
But . . . we've plenty more tricks up our sleeve.

Thérèse Tunney (10)
St Patrick's Primary School

I'M ANGRY

I'm Angry
I'm fed up
My blood is starting to boil
I'm going to explode
I just can't take it any more
I want to be free and happy
I want people to stop annoying me

I am furious
I am livid
I am offended
I just want people to stop making me Angry
I want them to leave me alone
I'm Angry.

Pam-Eileen McLean (11)
St Patrick's Primary School

ICE SKATING

I'm walking to the ice,
With my sharp, swift blade,
I gather my courage and I gather my speed,
Next minute I know, I have started my twirls and jumps,
One minute I'm jumping and next spinning
On the ice on my bum!
I get up and try again,
I jump . . . I twirl . . . I land . . .
I'm twirling like an angel,

Success
Strikes!

Eimeár McCoy (11)
St Patrick's Primary School

The Perfect Storm

When you think the night is going to be fine,
You've got another think coming.
First it gets cold,
Then it rains,
It gets harder till it turns to hail,
Then the wind blows hard,
Then clouds build up,
The wind blows hard as well as the hailstones,
The lightning strikes,
And the thunder bangs,
It gets closer and louder and bigger than before,
The wind spins,
A tornado,
It spins and spins,
It gets closer and closer,
I've been swooped up,
I'm spinning and spinning,
I've been knocked out,
When I wake up I'm in *Oz!*

Bronagh Kelly (11)
St Patrick's Primary School

I'M ANGRY

I don't want to do it!
I throw a tantrum,
I kick, I scream.
I feel as if the next
Person I see, I'd probably kill them!
My eyes water,
But I'm not crying.
My body feels clammy and warm.
Funny noises come out of my mouth
But I'm not laughing.
Someone listen ~ *I don't want to do it!*
I feel dizzy, my head's spinning
I'm frustrated and I'm *angry!*

Leona McAllister (11)
St Patrick's Primary School

I'M HAPPY

I'm bursting with joy
I just want to sing all day
I'm so excited
I'm glad to be at school with my friends
They help me with ABCs and 123s
I'm doing my best
I'm just bursting with joy
All day.

Donna Robinson (10)
St Patrick's Primary School

BOYS ARE . . .

Boys are the best, better than all the rest!
They will beat everyone whether it be a race or a run
Boys will do extreme sports like sky diving
Boys will do amazing stunts like jumping over seven cars on a
motorbike
They even are peacemakers (Martin Luther King)
Some seek great thrills (like me)
Some are mathematical geniuses (2+2=4)
Some are great at English (Hello)
Some are great at French (Bonjour) (Hello)
Some are class at Irish (Leathreas) (Toilet)
So just remember boys are the best, better than all the rest!

Kevin Agnew (11)
St Patrick's Primary School

EARTHQUAKE

E arth shakes violently
A nd perilously trembles
R aising death toll
T ragic events and newspaper stories
H omeless sleep on the street
Q ivering with fear
U sual life in the rich houses ~ what do they care?
A ges it will take to build up again ~
K ind charities help the survivors of the
E *arthquake.*

Maura O'Mullan (11)
St Patrick's Primary School

THE INSIDE OF A RAT

I've seen a rat,
Many times before,
But last week I saw more ~
The *inside* of a poor, disgusting rat.

Intestines that look like worms joining hands,
And stretch-like elastic bands,
His liver like a plum seed,
Like a wrinkly old granny's toe.

A heart that looks like a bud on a tree,
So round like a little ball,
If outside is ugly,
Don't view the inside.
Be warned!

Laura Glendinning (11)
St Patrick's Primary School

Girls Are . . . Boys Are . . .

Girls are hairclips and bows,
Boys are football mad and baseball caps,
Girls are posh and lovely,
Boys are gelled and spiked up hair,
Girls are thinking and moaning,
Boys are move on, let's get going,
Girls are Barbies and dolls,
Boys are muck and wrestling mad,
Girls are lipstick and body spray,
Boys are discos and tattoos.

James O'Kane (11)
St Patrick's Primary School

The Wonder Of Creation

I love all different kinds of weather
Raindrops falling amongst the heather
Sun that shines on hot desert sands
The wind that blows all round our lands.

I love the lamb born in the spring
The little bunnies and birds that sing
The caterpillar in his cocoon
Who'll turn into a butterfly soon.

I love the sea, I love the snow
I love all things that God made grow
The great oak tree that stands so tall
The little daisy, so simple and small.

From the mountain of Slemish
To Niagara Falls
God made them and I love them all.

Leanne Dickson (10)
St Patrick's Primary School

PARENTS ARE . . .

Parents are annoying 'Tidy your room.'
Parents are embarrassing 'Give me a nice, big hug!'
Parents are pathetic 'Who's Bryan McFadden?'*
Parents are boring 'When I was young . . .'
Parents are self-important 'That's *my* chair!'
Parents to *too* sensible 'It's bad for you.'
Parents are old-fashioned 'That woolly jumper's just lovely.'
Parents are stingy 'It's not worth the money.'

Parents are caring 'Put on your safety helmet.;
Parents are sharing 'You can have mine.'
Parents are daring 'Let's try the Ghost Train!'
Parents are money lenders 'Are you sure you have enough?'
Parents are funny 'Is there a mouse at the computer?'
Parents are clever 'I just booked tickets for the Westlife concert!'
Parents are hardworking 'I've just got my pay cheque.'
Parents are *cool!*

**Bryan McFadden is in Westlife.*

Helen Doherty (10)
St Patrick's Primary School

UP IN THE ATTIC

Up in the attic
          (and something's *creeping*)

A cobweb shivering
Water dripping
A tree tapping a window
Floorboards creaking
Mice scampering
Mousetraps snapping

Down in the cellar
          (and something's *rattling*)

Bones jangling
Chains clanking
Pipes dinking
Wind moaning eerily
Faint voices whispering
Heart thumping and thudding.

Mark McGuiggan (10)
St Patrick's Primary School

The Boat Bandit

The Boat Bandit
Was a thief
Who brought the money that he stole
To his big fat chief

The Bandit's a master
Of disguise
He'll dress up and rob you
In front of your eyes

The chief uses
The oodles of money
To achieve his dream
Of buying a million pots of honey

The Boat Bandit's
As cunning as a fox
As smart as an owl
And as strong as an ox

So watch he doesn't take
Your oodles of money
Or you will be left
With absolutely no honey.

Patrick Tunney (10)
St Patrick's Primary School

A Memory

This I remember,
I saw from the ground,
Flashes of thunder,
In the Boxing Night sky.

But then just like that,
The power had gone off.
I was scared stiff,
Alone in the dark.

As candles were lit,
I settled down,
Hoping with luck,
The power would come on.

Claire McMullan (9)
St Patrick's Primary School

SUPERSTITIONS

Beware of cracking any mirror,
or you'll have seven years bad luck,
and beware of a magpie,
Run, hide or else . . .

Eat an apple on *Hallowe'en*,
at midnight upon a mirror,
look over your shoulder,
and there you'll see your loved one!

Wear old socks unaware,
and there will be good luck,
try not to sleep above the kitchen
or it'll be bad luck,
and don't do a spider in.

Remember these with all you've got,
if not . . .

Donagh McAllister (9)
St Patrick's Primary School

December

I like days
With snow white blankets
And nights with
Glittering lights above
And children with noses
Like Rudolph play
And the moon is shining
Like a silver puddle in the sky.

I like days
When snowmen are standing
And snow is falling
Like moths in a flurry
And people are buying
Presents in a hurry
And you feel all warm
With Christmas coming.

Laura O'Kane (10)
St Patrick's Primary School

BOYS ARE, GIRLS ARE

Boys are strong and think they are tough
Girls are mummy's pets and look so beautiful
Boys are moving on 'Let's get on'
Girls are so posh and friendly
Boys look so handsome and smart
Girls look lovely in their blue and pink dress
Boys are football mad and hurling too
Girls are trendy and tall and also smart.

Sharon Kelly (11)
St Patrick's Primary School

DECEMBER

I like days
When the white blanket is on the street
And nights when the moon is high
And the stars are little silver dots
And the street lights are lit
And white figures in the garden
And everybody is wrapped up warm.

I like days
With trees glittering in the light
And fairy lights on the house
And Santa's outside
And the children play with the snow
With their noses red like Rudolph
And you feel all warm
With Christmas coming.

Caitriona Hasson (10)
St Patrick's Primary School

DECEMBER

I like days
with snow falling
from the sky
and at night stars
shining in the sky
The moon shining
like a gold coin
and icing topped
hills and the air
is cold.

Reece McLaughlin (9)
St Patrick's Primary School

Noises Outside School

Children yelling,
Balls banging on windows,
Birds singing,
Girls playing tig,
Boys playing football,
Nursery children shouting and having lots of fun,
People wailing and cutting their knees,
Teachers shouting,
Cars zooming down the street,
Just then the bell rings and
It's time to come in.

Catherine O'Kane (9)
St Patrick's Primary School

NOISE AT THE ZOO

Trumpet of an elephant.
Zebras neighing.
Lions and tigers roaring.
Monkeys chattering.
Seals honking.
Gorillas thumping their chests.
It's been the best.

Enda Drain (8)
St Patrick's Primary School

Noises In The Haunted House

These are the noises in the Haunted House,
Bats flying,
Spiders spinning their webs,
Doors slamming with the wind blowing
Stairs creaking,
Roaring fire in the fireplace,
Spooky bedrooms,
Ghost noises coming from the attic
Pictures of people looking at you everywhere you go
Dust everywhere,
Saucepans falling,
Gates squeaking outside,
Mice running around,
Who lives in this Haunted House?
No one knows.

Ryan Doherty (9)
St Patrick's Primary School

Noises In My Bus

Everyone is shouting
Thumping their feet
Crisp bags crunching
Children yelling
P1s crying
Everyone squealing
People taking markers
Out and squeaking them
All over the windows.
The bright sun
Coming in the window
P7s open the sunroof
And you can just
About hear the birds
Whistling.

If you want a noisy bus
Come to me
And I'll show you mine.

Clare Kelly (8)
St Patrick's Primary School

NOISES AT HOME

People talking
Cats meowing
TV blaring
Shower pouring
Dinner cooking
Crisp bags crunching
Angel thumping
Around the house
Cars driving past
Birds in the loft
Piano playing
Tin whistle playing
Flute playing
It's quite noisy in my house.

Meghan Rafferty (9)
St Patrick's Primary School

NOISES IN THE HAUNTED HOUSE

Doors creaking.
Smashing windows.
Shouting, squealing.
Black cats meow.
Creepy music.
Bats flying.
Thumping feet bump.
Creepy whistling.
Creepy noises.
Creepy birds making noises.
Dripping water. Drip! Drip!
Wood falling.
Chimney cracking. Crack! Crack!
Light shade dangling.
It's spooky here!

Terry O'Boyle (9)
St Patrick's Primary School

Noises In The Classroom

People shouting
Teacher scolding
Pencil pots falling
Telephone ringing
Chairs creaking
Bells ringing
P1s crying
Doors banging
People thumping
People sharpening
Children fighting
It's *noisy!*

Eugene McTaggart (8)
St Patrick's Primary School

My Colour Poem

Silver is the starry glistening night,
The sparkling ring on my finger,
Icy icicles clinging
From the bare winter trees.

Gold are the stripes
On the purring pussycat,
The golden shining sun,
And the tender juicy peach.

White is the glittering frost,
On the ground,
The friendly snowman dancing,
In the snow all around.

Blue is the cold pond,
On the quiet country road,
The summer's warm sunny sky,
The colour of my sparkling blue eyes.

Emma McKay (8)
The Diamond Primary School

Colours

Red is like a roaring motorbike,
All dark against the moonlight,
Or a juicy red apple,
Just waiting for us to bite.

White is like a little lamb,
Jumping and skipping in the long grass,
Or a white fluffy cloud,
In the blue sky above us.

Gold is like a ring on a finger,
Or the sun shining in the sky,
Like gold coins gleaming all so bright,
And corn shivering in the wind.

Jason Harkness (8)
The Diamond Primary School

Colours

Black is a cat running in the moonlight,
Like a burglar which will be a nasty sight,
Really thick black smoke,
Black is the colour of fizzy coke.

White is the colour of the falling snow,
Or the colour of someone's cold toe,
Two polar bears all cold and white,
Having a really big fight.

Gold is the colour of the shining sun.
Two children outside having great fun,
Gold is the colour of a shiny pound,
Which one lucky boy found.

Andrew Byers (8)
The Diamond Primary School

WHITE

White is for cold, drifting snow,
Falling from the sky,
Or big fluffy polar bears at the South Pole,
Cold snowflakes and deep white snow.

Stuart Thompson (8)
The Diamond Primary School

THE COLOUR WHITE

White is like a sheep's wool,
As white as your granny's hair,
A snowman in the snow,
The cold winter air.

Amy Greer (8)
The Diamond Primary School

My Favourite Colours

Grey is a seal balancing on a bouncy ball,
Like a big fat snail that eats wriggly worms,
And old man's hair that was never combed,
Like an old bear that has no eyes.

Orange is a big, fat juicy fruit,
Like a freezing cold ice-lolly,
Like a warm cosy fire,
Like a big, bright umbrella.

Beverley Kerr (8)
The Diamond Primary School

A World Without Trees

Imagine a world without trees
Never seeing the golden orange leaves.
Never hearing the fierce storms at night.
No home for the poor little robins or blackbirds.
No place for the cool shade from the blazing hot sun.
No paper, furniture or oxygen ~ not even books to read!

Zoey Peacock (11)
The Diamond Primary School

A World Without Trees

Imagine a world without trees
Never seeing rosy pink blossoms falling lightly in the wind.
Never hearing spring birds singing happily to themselves.
No home for helpless little animals.
No place for snoozing under the lovely shade.
No more lovely sounds or books to read.

Hollie Thompson (11)
The Diamond Primary School